ILLEGAL

For Jackie, Finn and Seán – EC

For Viv, Lexie and Fisher – AD

For Paola, always – GR

ILLEGAL

EOIN COLFER
ANDREW DONKIN

ART BY GIOVANNI RIGANO

LETTERING BY CHRIS DICKEY

HODDER CHILDREN'S BOOKS

First published in Great Britain in 2017 by Hodder and Stoughton

3 5 7 9 10 8 6 4 2

A CIP catalogue record for this book
is available from the British Library.

HB ISBN 978 1 444 93400 7
TPB ISBN 978 1 444 94198 2

Printed and bound in China

The paper and board used in this book
are made from wood from responsible sources.

Hodder Children's Books
An imprint of
Hachette Children's Group
Part of Hodder and Stoughton
Carmelite House
50 Victoria Embankment
London EC4Y 0DZ

An Hachette UK Company
www.hachette.co.uk

www.hachettechildrens.co.uk

"YOU, WHO ARE SO-CALLED ILLEGAL ALIENS, MUST KNOW THAT NO HUMAN BEING IS ILLEGAL. THAT IS A CONTRADICTION IN TERMS. HUMAN BEINGS CAN BE BEAUTIFUL OR MORE BEAUTIFUL, THEY CAN BE FAT OR SKINNY, THEY CAN BE RIGHT OR WRONG, BUT ILLEGAL? HOW CAN A HUMAN BEING BE ILLEGAL?"

ELIE WIESEL
NOBEL LAUREATE AND
HOLOCAUST SURVIVOR

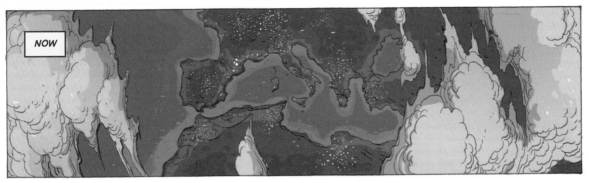

NOW

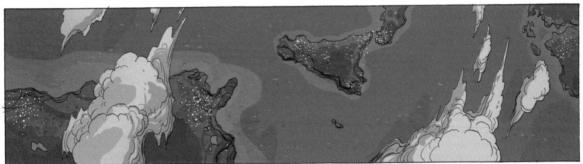

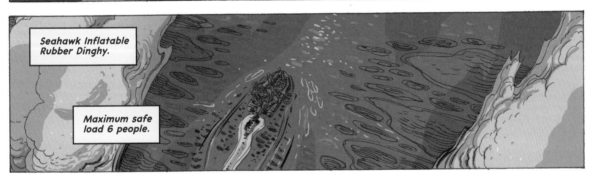

Seahawk Inflatable Rubber Dinghy.

Maximum safe load 6 people.

Currently carrying 14 passengers.

THIS IS YOUR FAULT, EBO.

I'VE TOLD YOU, LEAVE HIM ALONE.

1

2

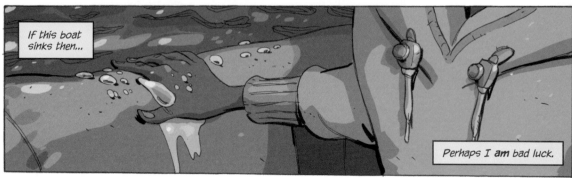

The men showed us a photograph of a better boat. Shining and new with space for all.

Not this rotten, patched-up thing. Kwame tried to argue, but the men would not listen.

BDAM!
BDAM!
BDAM!

MOVE OR THERE'S A BULLET IN YOUR BACK!

STOP!

WHY ARE WE FIGHTING?

KWAME, PLEASE.

WE ALL HAVE THE SAME DESTINATION.

DESTINATION? HE'S NOT HOLDING IT STRAIGHT AND ALREADY WE'RE LOST.

WE'RE NOT LOST.

RAZAK IS DOING A FINE JOB.

I KEEP THE MOON ON MY LEFT. THIS IS HOW I NAVIGATE.

IT WAS ON THE RIGHT WHEN WE FIRST SAILED.

THEN

Nineteen months earlier

He's gone.

Without even a word.

Kwame, my brother, is gone.

EBO, COME! SING A SONG FOR THE LITTLE ONES. YOUR VOICE MAKES THEM SO CALM.

CHAPTER 2

"I AM SORRY, TEACHER. NOT NOW."

Perhaps Kwame is still in the village.

Market.

Football pitch.

Maybe the old well.

With the other boys.

HAVE YOU...

FORGET IT, EBO. HE'S GONE ALREADY.

HE GOT ON THE DAWN BUS.

CAN IT BE THAT YOUR ONLY BROTHER LEFT FOREVER AND DID NOT TELL YOU, EBO?

PERHAPS HE DOESN'T CARE ABOUT YOU.

HE'LL BE SWALLOWED BY THE DESERT SANDS JUST LIKE YOUR SISTER BEFORE.

I WONDER WHAT BROTHEL SHE'S WORKING IN NOW, EBO?

WHAT?

THAT'S WHY YOU HAVEN'T HEARD FROM HER. SISI IS VERY BUSY.

DON'T WORRY. I BET KWAME IS HAPPY ENOUGH. HE'LL PROBABLY MISTAKE THE FIRST PUDDLE HE FINDS FOR THE SEA AND THINK HE'S IN EUROPE ALREADY.

POOR EBO, ALL ALONE. WHO WILL PROTECT YOU NOW?

They are like mean little children.

8

I start to sing.

MY FRIEND THE BIRD SINGS ITS SWEET SONG... I WOKE UP THIS MORNING... MY FRIEND WAS GONE

It's what they expect.

HE *CAN* SING. YOU HAVE TO ADMIT THAT.

NOW AFTER MORNING COMES THE DAY... IS MY FRIEND SINGING FAR FAR AWAY?

ALWAYS.

FAR FAR AWAY.

OMPH!

DO NOT TALK ABOUT SISI.

AGGH.

THAT IS THE WRONG NOTE.

LEAVE THE SINGING TO ME.

He's drunk now.

And there's blood on his shirt again.

YOU LOOKING FOR YOUR BROTHER?

He knows.

HE'S GONE. LEFT YOU AND WENT.

YOU CAN'T BLAME HIM. THERE'S NOTHING HERE FOR HIM.

HELP ME GET INSIDE.

YOU REMEMBER LAURENCE? HE SOLD KWAME A PLACE ON HIS BUS FOR AGADEZ.

YOUR BROTHER'S A GOOD WORKER, BUT HE'S NOT THE SMARTEST, AND HE THINKS HE SHOULD TRY FOR EUROPE!

DO YOU THINK HE CAN MAKE IT?

I HOPE SO. IF HE SENDS MONEY THEN I WON'T HAVE TO WORK SO HARD EVERY DAY TAKING CARE OF YOU.

WHEN WE GET INSIDE, YOU'LL NEED TO HELP CLEAN ME.

"NOW THAT KWAME IS GONE THERE WILL BE LESS TIME TO WASTE SINGING. MORE WORK TO BE DONE."

I get him into his bed as fast as I can.

I've done it.

There's no queue at the Depot.

There's no hope.

He's gone.

NOW

The dawn sun warms us at last.

CHAPTER 3

THE ENGINE IS MAKING THAT STRANGE NOISE AGAIN. IT'S NOT THE NOISE OF A HAPPY ENGINE.

IT MEANS THAT THE ENGINE IS THIRSTY. AS WE ARE. AND THERE IS NOTHING LEFT FOR ANY OF US.

Razak kept steering until he could no longer feel his hands.

EVEN WITH WHAT WE PAID, THEY DID NOT GIVE US ENOUGH FUEL TO MAKE THE JOURNEY.

Then we took turns through the night.

By mid-morning the sun is baking us and we have to make our own shade on the boat.

WE SHOULD HAVE BROUGHT UMBRELLAS.

WE SHOULD HAVE BROUGHT PETROL.

PETROL AND UMBRELLAS!

The engine chokes and dies...

RAZAK?

WHAT?

WHY ARE YOU SMILING?

IT'S NOTHING.

TELL US!

I WAS JUST THINKING I WONDER IF CHELSEA ARE PLAYING TONIGHT.

AH! CHELSEA! HE LOVES THEM!

I THINK HE WOULD RATHER *THEY* WERE IN THE BOAT WITH HIM THAN *US*.

I DON'T WANT TO PLAY FOR THEM BECAUSE THEN THEY WOULD LOSE!

THERE'S NOT ROOM!

MAYBE ONE DAY YOU'LL PLAY FOR THEM?

BUT ONE DAY I WOULD LIKE TO BE A COMMENTATOR FOR THE BBC WORLD SERVICE — IT WOULD BE MY DREAM.

I WOULD SAY EVERYTHING HAPPENING ON THE PITCH VERY CLEARLY. I HAVE EYES LIKE THE DESERT HAWK.

YOU WOULD BE GREAT.

WE'RE TRYING TO SLEEP.

IS THERE ANY WATER LEFT?

NO, IT'S ALL FINISHED.

YOU WOULD BE THE BEST COMMENTATOR OF ALL.

IT'S BEEN A TRICKY FIRST HALF FOR OUR BRAVE PLAYERS, BUT THINGS COULD TURN AROUND IN THE SECOND HALF.

SPLASH

"WOAH!"

"SING FOR THEM, EBO. TELL THEM OF OUR COUNTRY."

MY HOME IS IN MY HEART... I DREAM OF IT EVERY NIGHT...

I SEE ITS RIVERS MIGHTY BENEATH THE STARS SO BRIGHT...

"LOOK AT THEM. THEY DON'T NEED A SONG."

"LET'S PADDLE."

THEN

CHAPTER 4

I know where I have to go.

I must find my brother. And together we will find Sisi.

I take what's mine. It's not much.

I know Uncle Patrick has money for drink hidden in the mattress.

I leave it there.

It feels like a door has opened. And that I need to step through before it closes.

EBO?

EBO? ARE YOU GOING TO AGADEZ? WHY?

I HAVE TO FIND MY BROTHER.

DO YOU HAVE MONEY FOR YOUR FARE?

"I CAN FIND WORK WHEN I AM IN AGADEZ AND GET YOU THE MONEY FOR NEXT WEEK."

WAAAA-HHHHHHH!

I KNOW HOW THINGS ARE WITH YOUR UNCLE, BUT I CAN'T JUST...

YOU WOULD NOT LIKE TRAVELLING ANYWAY.

WE DRIVE THROUGH THE NIGHT AND IT'S NOT GOING TO BE PLEASANT.

WAAAA-HHHHHHH!

WAAAA-HHHHHHH!

"EBO?"

20

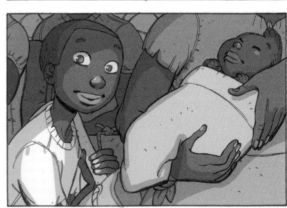

21

I believe they do not sell tickets for the roof because I now know that no one could survive the bumps.

The bus crawls through the night.

The air somehow grows hotter without the sun.

The land is a vast oven.

I can't sleep, but at least every single hole in the road is taking me closer to Kwame.

The bus pulls in and for the first time, I am scared...

Even the air smells different here. Burnt.

My hand trembles when I show the photograph.

I DO NOT REMEMBER HIM. I AM SORRY.

"NO." "NO."

"NO."

OH YES... I REMEMBER.

JUST YESTERDAY.

CAN YOU TELL ME WHERE HE WENT? PLEASE?

HE SAID HE WAS GOING TO EUROPE TO GET A BIG HELICOPTER FOR HIS LITTLE BROTHER.

PLEASE CAN YOU TELL ME WHERE HE WENT?

16°58'0"N
7°59'0"E

AGADEZ – largest city
in central Niger. It lies
towards the south of
the Sahara Desert.

"*THIS* IS
AGADEZ..."

"IT'S SO
HUGE..."

HA...
I REMEMBER
AGADEZ WHEN
IT WAS HALF
THE SIZE IT IS
TODAY.

NOW IT'S FULL
OF PEOPLE LIKE YOU.
PEOPLE WHO ARE WORKING,
SAVING, WAITING FOR THEIR
TIME TO CROSS THE DESERT.
MANY GOING TOWARDS
EUROPE.

WAS
YOUR BROTHER
MEETING
SOMEONE IN
AGADEZ?

I DON'T
KNOW.

DOES HE
HAVE FRIENDS
HERE?

I DON'T
KNOW.

WELL,
I'M CERTAIN
YOU'LL LOCATE
YOUR BROTHER
VERY SOON.

I look at Agadez and my heart falls. It's so big.

How can I ever find anyone here?

25

I make a shelter from the morning sun. So for a moment, I can rest.

So far I have swapped a hut at home for a patch of empty wall.

If he could see me, Uncle Patrick would be laughing now.

People always need bottles.

Always.

The sign says "LABOUR BY HOUR".

I'M STRONGER THAN I LOOK. MUCH STRONGER. I CAN WORK.

DO YOU HAVE A TICKET?

TICKET?

ROUND THE BACK...

27

So far, this is not much of a new life.

I have to find Kwame.

MINE!

Adrift in this dark, dark place.

I have to find my brother.

Water is coming into the boat.

GET THE WATER OUT QUICKLY! USE YOUR HANDS! USE ANYTHING!

There must be a hole or a rip in the floor.

IT'S COMING IN FASTER.

GET IT OUT OR WE WILL SINK.

I feel the floor of the dinghy. Gently.

There's a small split.

However fast we bail it out, more will come in.

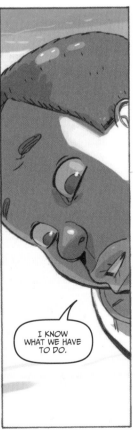

I KNOW WHAT WE HAVE TO DO.

EBO, DON'T STOP! KEEP GOING.

I KNOW WHAT WE HAVE TO DO.

HOWEVER FAST WE GET THE WATER OUT, MORE WILL COME.

WE NEED TO TURN THE BOAT OVER.

WHAT?

EBO, WE'RE NOT TURNING THE BOAT UPSIDE DOWN.

NO, HE'S RIGHT. WE CAN CLIMB ON AND THE RIP WILL BE OUT OF THE WATER.

OH GOD.

I CAN'T SWIM.

RAZAK, NONE OF US CAN SWIM.

I go under.

The voices above me are muffled to silence.

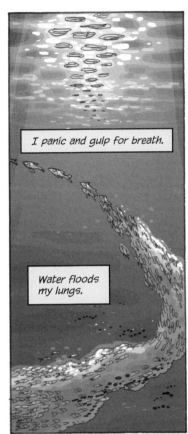

I panic and gulp for breath.

Water floods my lungs.

I freeze.

All I can do is think how beautiful the fish are.

A hand grabs me from behind.

I gasp for life.

I HAVE YOU, EBO.

Somehow we have all survived.

THANK YOU, THANK YOU FOR SAVING ME.

I AM AFRAID YOU ARE NOT MUCH BETTER OFF.

We have no food, water, or petrol.

We are drifting on the tides, lost and alone.

WE'RE GOING TO DIE, AREN'T WE?

DON'T SAY IT, EBO. WE CAN'T GIVE UP. EVER. SISI WAITS FOR US.

THEN

THE MARKETPLACE, AGADEZ

CHAPTER 6

I look at every face in case one is my brother.

None of them is.

I can't even be sure that Kwame is still here.

If he had money, he could have paid for passage north across the desert.

Maybe he's already gone.

I need food.

I need money.

I need work.

YOU. AGAIN?

"THERE'S NOTHING FOR YOU HERE."

Each day I try for work.

Each day I look for my brother in every face.

HEY! YOU'VE...

The packets say "Antiseptic Wipes".

There must be a use for these.

EARLY EVENING

People come back to their homes.

I see Penn cooking. I've seen him in the work lines.

His leg looks hurt.

Maybe I can make a trade.

37

I make myself as useful as I can the next night.

I get a smile and a small pot of food.

Penn has many friends here.

DO YOU KNOW SOMEWHERE HE CAN FIND DAY WORK?

Soon, I have friends too.

I make the wipes last as long as I can.

The wipes came to me for nothing. So sometimes if someone has no food I do a clean for free.

And I make another friend.

I join in people's songs around the fire.

I REMEMBER HIM. HE SANG ON MY BUS WHEN I CAME HERE.

One night, people give me food just for the song.

THE BAKO TREE... THE BAKO TREE... REACHES TO THE SKY...

SO FAR... SO FAR...THE NESTING BIRDS SING TO THE STARS

Just for the singing.

I like this exchange.

A week turns into a month.

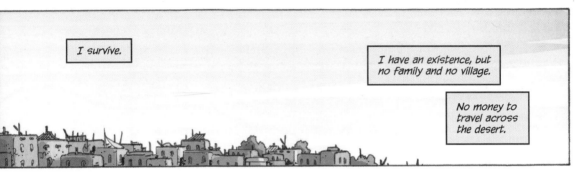

I survive.

I have an existence, but no family and no village.

No money to travel across the desert.

Kwame may be hundreds of miles away by now.

"THERE HE IS."

MY FRIEND HAS HURT HIMSELF. HE NEEDS ONE OF YOUR WIPES.

WHERE IS HE INJURED?

HE NEEDS *ALL* OF YOUR WIPES.

WHAT?

NOW!

Trouble.

THAT'S HIM!

YOU SANG ON THE BUS WHEN WE CAME TO AGADEZ.

WE NEED A SINGER RIGHT NOW OR MY WEDDING WILL BE RUINED.

PLEASE WILL YOU COME?

WE CAN PAY YOU...

WILL YOU...

IT WOULD BE MY GREAT HONOUR.

I grab my bag. That's everything I have. And we go.

WHAT HAPPENED TO YOUR SINGER?

HE HAS A PROBLEM.

YES, THE PROBLEM IS THAT HE'S AN IDIOT.

"HE KISSED THE BRIDESMAID AND UPSET HER FIANCÉ."

"OH."

I CAN DILL DING.

HERE, FRIEND... YOU NEED THIS MORE THAN I DO.

COME ON, EBO...

I hear the crowd...

NOW

I hold on tight to Kwame.

Around us, the night is pitch black.

CHAPTER 7

I hold on to Kwame and I don't let go.

We drift in and out of banks of mist, clinging to the upside-down dinghy for our lives.

I'M F-F-F-FRREEZZZING.

Everyone is soaking wet and shivering with cold.

WE DON'T KNOW WHERE WE ARE, DO WE, EBO?

WE ARE ON OUR WAY, THAT'S WHERE WE ARE.

THINGS COULD BE WORSE FOR US.

WORSE? HOW COULD THINGS BE WORSE?

RAZAK, DO NOT LET GO!

I'M NOT GOING TO. BUT SOON MY HANDS WILL DO IT FOR ME.

WE TRIED OUR BEST FOR EUROPE, BUT EVERYTHING WAS AGAINST US.

KEEP HOLD, RAZAK, PLEASE.

I'M NOT GOING TO. I...

CAN YOU HEAR THAT?

WHAT?

THERE'S A SOUND.

YES, THE WAVES.

NO, LISTEN!

"THERE'S SOMETHING IN THE MIST..."

A boat suddenly emerges...

No lights, because they do not want to be seen.

It's huge compared to our little dinghy.

There must be hundreds on board.

I hear someone gasp
and realise it's me.

Suddenly it feels like we're saved, but we're not.

WE HAVE TO MAKE THEM SEE US.

But it's a chance.

HEY!

OVER HERE!

HELP US PLEASE!

CAREFUL, DON'T TIP US OVER.

WE NEED TO SHOUT TOGETHER.

"ONE, TWO, THREE..."

HELP!

DID THEY HEAR US?

If the captain doesn't stop, we are dead.

THEN

It takes us twenty-one weeks to save enough for two fares across the desert.

Twenty-one weeks. Sisi will be different now. She could be married.

MOST PEOPLE HAVE TO STAY MUCH LONGER, EBO. WE SHOULD BE HAPPY.

PAS UN PAS SANS VISA

CHAPTER 8

I *AM* HAPPY.

I'M STILL HAPPY THAT I EVEN FOUND YOU AGAIN. WE WERE MEANT TO MAKE THIS JOURNEY TOGETHER.

I KNOW.

DO YOU REMEMBER THE RULES WE HEARD FOR TRAVELLING IN THE DESERT?

EBO, CALM YOURSELF.

THERE ISN'T EVEN ANYONE ELSE IN THE QUEUE YET. WE'LL BE FIRST ON THE TRUCK SO WE CAN GET A GOOD SHADY SPOT.

WHAT IS THAT? IS IT A HOUSE ON THE ROAD?

WHAT?

It's not a house...

We have to get on.

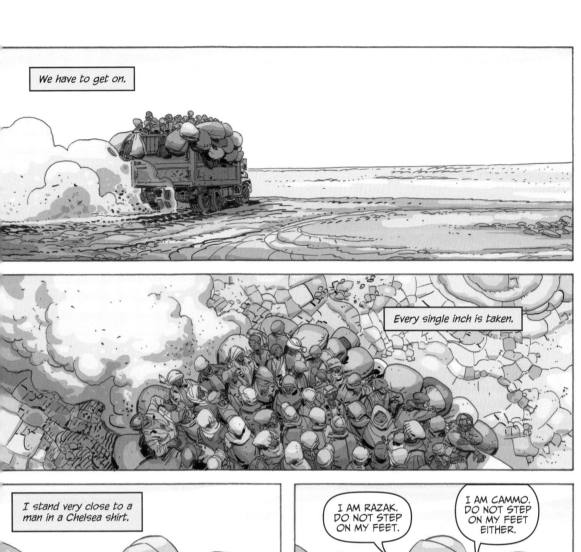

Every single inch is taken.

I stand very close to a man in a Chelsea shirt.

I AM RAZAK. DO NOT STEP ON MY FEET.

I AM CAMMO. DO NOT STEP ON MY FEET EITHER.

He does not seem like he wishes to talk about football.

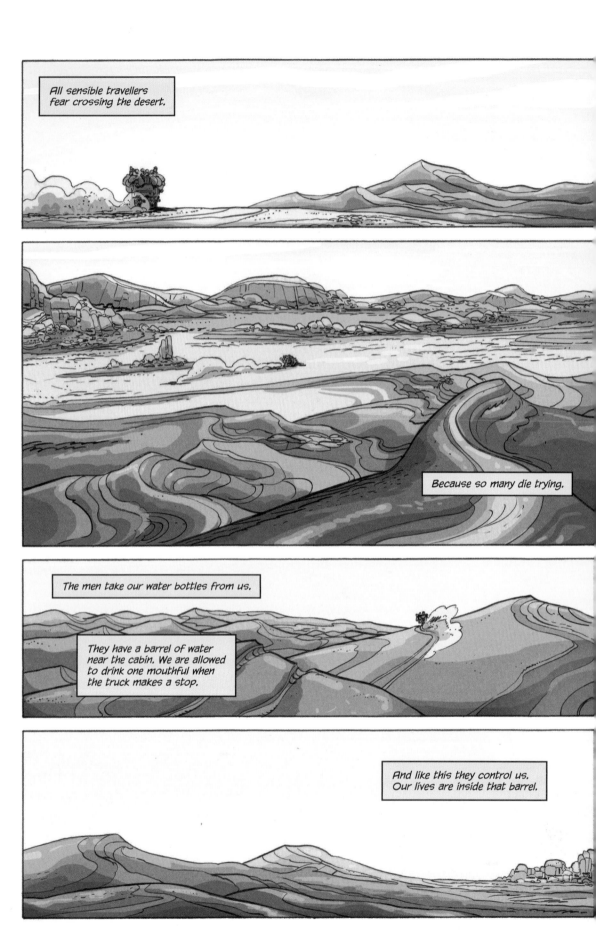

All sensible travellers fear crossing the desert.

Because so many die trying.

The men take our water bottles from us.

They have a barrel of water near the cabin. We are allowed to drink one mouthful when the truck makes a stop.

And like this they control us. Our lives are inside that barrel.

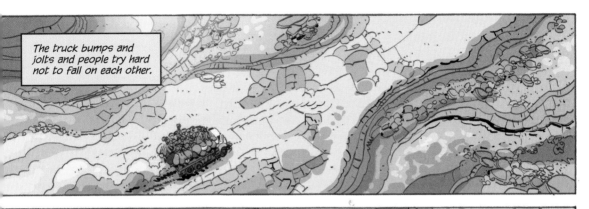

The truck bumps and jolts and people try hard not to fall on each other.

I hope the truck is strong enough to carry us all.

With so little water, it gets hard to swallow and...

Oh...

STOP!

A man has fallen.

55

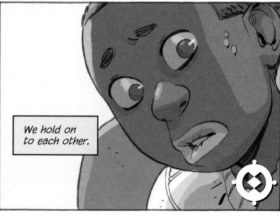

NOW

"HAVE THEY SEEN US?"

We shout. We wave.

The ship cuts its engines.

And slows.

CHAPTER 9

THEY'VE FOUND US JUST IN TIME...

YES, IF...

WHAT DO YOU MEAN "IF..."? IF WHAT?

THEY *MUST* HELP US.

WE ARE PEOPLE.

"PADDLE QUICKLY SO WE DO NOT MISS OUR CHANCE."

WHAT ARE YOU GOING TO DO?

I see faces look over the side of the boat.

Kwame keeps saying, "They have to help us", over and over and over.

We are all so cold. So cold and tired.

PLEASE...

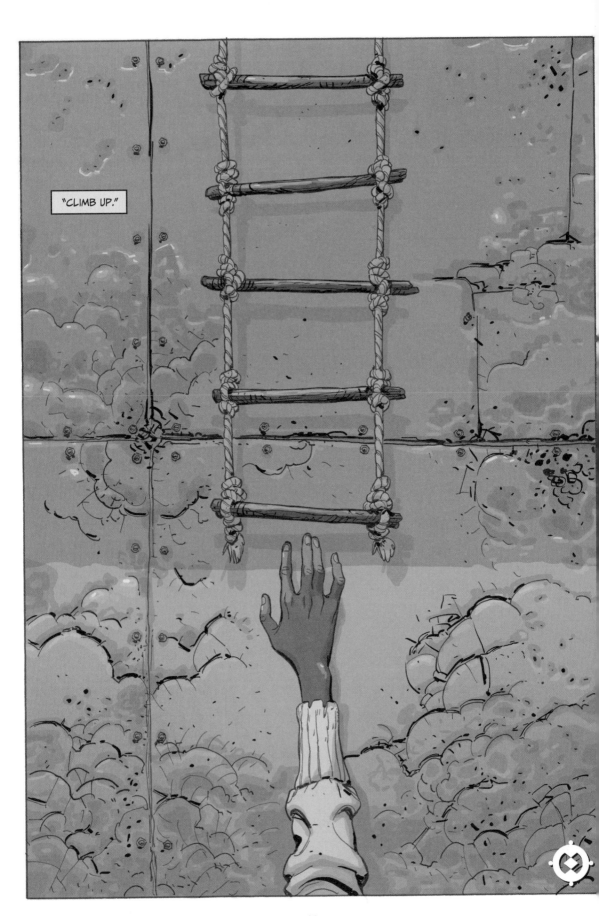

THEN

For the first day, water was free.

Now, it's not.

CHAPTER 10

THAT'S TWENTY A CUP.

BUT THAT'S MORE THAN THIS MORNING.

THERE'S LESS WATER LEFT THAN THIS MORNING.

There's a rumbling sound that gets louder.

KWAME?

STAY BEHIND ME, LITTLE BROTHER.

The men in the jeeps are angry.

⟨ WHERE HAVE YOU BEEN?! WE WAITED HERE FOR YOU FOR TWO HOURS! IDIOT! ⟩*

*Libyan Arabic

⟨ WE HAD TO CHANGE ANOTHER TYRE! YOU TRY IT, IF YOU THINK YOU CAN DO IT FASTER! ⟩

⟨ THIS DESERT RUINS EVERY VEHICLE I USE. ⟩

THIS IS NOT GOOD.

⟨ I NEED TO RETURN. LOAD UP THE TRUCK WITH THE CARTONS. QUICKLY! ⟩

No one argues.

We move all the cartons from the jeeps into the truck.

‹ I'LL HAVE THE SAME FOR YOU NEXT RUN. BUT THE PRICE WILL BE MORE. ›

‹ MORE? ›

GET BACK ON!

But now, there's not enough room.

‹ YOU'RE FULL. DRIVE ON AND WE'LL TAKE THE REST BACK WITH US FOR ANOTHER TRUCK. ›

‹ OK. ›

INTO JEEP!

The truck moves away, leaving us behind...

This is not what we paid for, but at least we are not being left in the desert to die.

〈 COME ON! WORK... 〉

〈 STUPID STUPID MACHINE! 〉

He cannot get the engine to work.

The man leaves his jeep.

His passengers don't know what to do.

〈 IT WON'T START, I'LL COME WITH YOU. 〉

OUT!

NOW

People are so kind.

CHAPTER 11

EBO, ARE YOU OK?

I CAN START TO FEEL MY FINGERS AGAIN...

...A LITTLE.

Although they hardly have anything, people give us blankets.

Someone passes us water.

DRINK SLOWLY, EBO, OR YOU MIGHT BE ILL.

I drink quickly.

I can't help it.

THANK YOU... THANK YOU SO MUCH.

I HOPE YOU BRING THIS SHIP LUCK.

YOU MUST BE A LUCKY PERSON TO BE FOUND IN THIS BIG OCEAN.

Right now, I do feel lucky.

The ship set sail from the Libyan coast twelve hours ago.

There's not an inch of spare deck space.

70

Everything smells of oil. Oil and people.

For the first time in days, I can't hear the waves.

Everywhere is the hum of the engines and people's voices.

"I WILL DO ANYTHING TO REACH EUROPE."

"I JUST WANT TO SEE MY SON AGAIN."

"I HAD TO LEAVE MY HOME. THE WAR CAME."

"I WANT TO MAKE A GOOD LIFE FOR MY CHILDREN."

"MY UNCLE WORKS IN A RESTAURANT IN NAPLES. HE CAN GET ME A JOB."

"I WOULD LIKE WORK IN A SCHOOL."

People are pushed so close together.

A women leans into me like she's falling.

She's nearly asleep on her feet.

⟨ I'M SORRY. ⟩*

ARE YOU ALL RIGHT?

* Yoruba

I don't understand her words, but her face says, "Hold my baby".

⟨ YOU LOOK LIKE A GOOD BOY. COULD YOU PLEASE HOLD MY BABY UNTIL MY HUSBAND RETURNS? ⟩

⟨ I NEED TO REST FOR A MOMENT. ⟩

⟨ HE IS EIGHT WEEKS OLD AND HE FEEDS SO MUCH. ⟩

He is so small.

And looks so peaceful.

Sleeping while everything happens around him.

⟨ WHY ARE YOU HOLDING MY BABY?!! ⟩

WHAT?

⟨ WHAT HAVE YOU DONE TO MY WIFE? ⟩

⟨ I'M HERE. I'M FINE. THIS BOY IS HELPING ME FOR A MOMENT. I WAS SO TIRED. ⟩

⟨ IT'S OK? ⟩

⟨ I'M SORRY. I DIDN'T KNOW. WE'RE SO TIRED. PLEASE EXCUSE ME. ⟩

⟨ THANK YOU FOR HELPING MY WIFE. THE BABY IS EXHAUSTING HER. ⟩

They are a family.

They need to stay together.

THEN

We stare at the horizon, at the spot where the jeep disappeared.

OK, SO WE WALK.

WE STAY TOGETHER AND WE WALK.

WHAT?

CHAPTER 12

WE HAVE BEEN TRAVELLING FOR DAYS. WE MUST BE MOST OF THE WAY ACROSS THE DESERT.

LET'S FOLLOW THE TYRE TRACKS OF THE TRUCK.

WE WALK. IT'S THAT OR DIE HERE.

MAYBE THEY WILL COME BACK?

THEY'RE NOT COMING BACK.

CAMMO IS RIGHT. THE DESERT CANNOT BE SO BIG.

I AGREE WITH CAMMO.

We walk.

We walk.

We walk more.

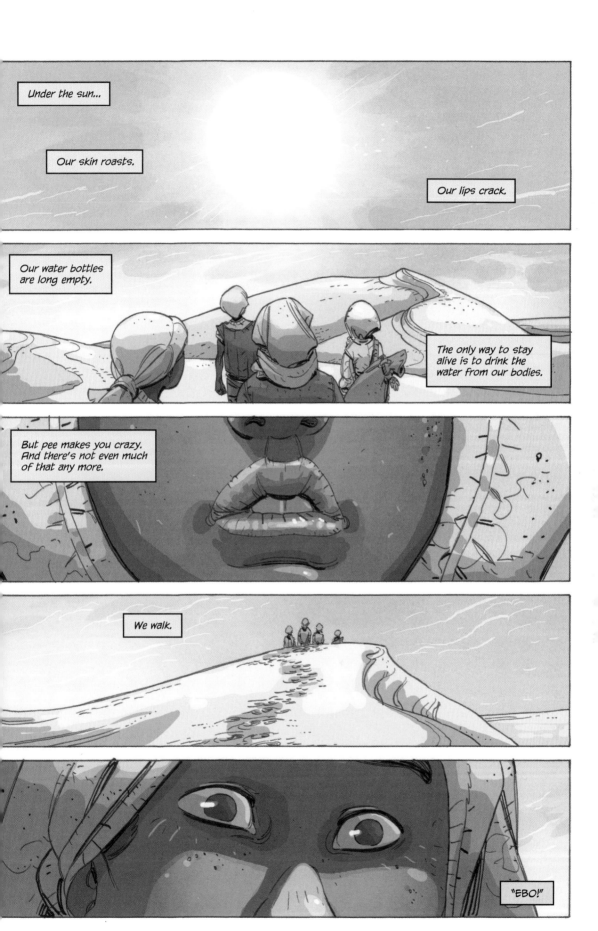

Under the sun...

Our skin roasts.

Our lips crack.

Our water bottles are long empty.

The only way to stay alive is to drink the water from our bodies.

But pee makes you crazy. And there's not even much of that any more.

We walk.

"EBO!"

THEY'RE DEAD. THEY CAN'T SAVE US.

EBO? COME ON, LET'S KEEP WALKING.

THEY MIGHT HAVE WATER.

YOU CANNOT DISTURB THE DEAD.

It would be stupid not to look. We could be lucky.

I'M SMALL.

MAYBE THE DEAD WON'T NOTICE ME.

Please.

Anything.

"YES!"

79

The bottles are still sealed.

They must be safe.

We drink anyway.

THIS IS DEAD MAN'S WATER.

CAMMO, PLEASE...

MAYBE WE SHOULD REST HERE IN THE JEEP, UNTIL IT'S NIGHT?

THEN WALK WHEN IT'S COOLER?

HE'S RIGHT. IT'S A GOOD IDEA.

I'M TOO TIRED TO FIGHT OFF EVIL SPIRITS.

YOU REST WITH THE BONE MEN.

I'LL REST UNDERNEATH.

I hug a bottle of water and close my eyes.

I wake up shivering.

It's freezing.

IT'S SO COLD.

BECAUSE WE SLEPT TOO LONG.

WE NEED TO START WALKING TO MAKE OURSELVES WARM.

CAMMO! WAKE UP, IT'S TIME TO GO.

"CAMMO?"

Cammo does not wake up. Perhaps the cold finished him. Perhaps he was simply too tired.

Razak wants to stay and bury him with respect.

But the desert ground is too hard. And we are too tired.

We cover Cammo with a cloth and we say some words, then...

...we walk.

NOW

Morning.

Everyone is hungry and thirsty.

CHAPTER 13

Now all they want is land.

All any of us want is Europe.

Low clouds cover the sky ahead of us.

One of them has a heartbeat.

THUMP
THUMP
THUMP

The heartbeat gets louder...

Deeper...

Until it thuds in our chests and we see it...

The helicopter bursts out of the clouds.

Engines deafen us.

People gasp.

Shout for help.

People wave scarves, clothes, whatever they're holding.

The helicopter dives low and thunders over the boat.

Wind ripples our faces.

Europe.

GET BACK!

The ship leans badly.

The captain orders us to move away from the side.

People struggle to stay on their feet.

But we do it.

The ship steadies...

The woman says thank you.

⟨ THANK YOU. ⟩

I think.

LOOK.

LOOK!

THE SHIP IS HERE.

WHEN WE GET TO LAND, WE MUST ALL STAY TOGETHER.

ME, YOU, RAZAK, NURU.

OF COURSE.

"WE DID THE CROSSING TOGETHER, EBO, AND WE'LL MAKE A NEW LIFE TOGETHER."

People move to see the new ship.

Too many.

"BUT WE'RE NOT ON DRY LAND YET, KWAME."

"NOT YET, BUT IT WON'T BE LONG."

There's a groan of metal straining.

AGGGH!

The rail snaps and a man falls.

Then more.

And a second later...

...so do we.

THEN

TRIPOLI – NORTH AFRICA, ON THE MEDITERRANEAN SEA

CHAPTER 14

After the desert, we'd never been so pleased to see water.

We drank all day. Until we started pissing again.

It hurt.

After the desert, I got ill.

But that didn't stop us. We worked, then paid for a ride from town to town.

Then we worked more and paid for another ride.

Then another.

Until we made it here...

...to Tripoli.

We must reach Tripoli to catch a boat — the only way to Europe.

LET'S SEE YOUR PAPERS.

AND YOUR MONEY.

OR YOU CAN GO BACK WHERE YOU CAME FROM.

STOP

The checkpoint is to keep people who do not have the right papers out of the city.

We do not have **any** papers.

I feel so cold.

Shivering.

Sweating.

I feel cold, but Kwame says I am much too hot.

We hear one of the soldiers searching.

No one breathes.

After a long time, we move.

And I'm still shivering when we get out.

THIS IS THE END OF THE LINE. YOU'VE HAD YOUR JOURNEY.

BECAUSE OF THE EXTRA SOLDIERS AROUND TODAY, THERE WILL BE A SURCHARGE.

WHAT?!

YOU DON'T HAVE TO PAY IT. WE CAN TAKE YOU TO THE POLICE.

IT'S NOT FAIR.

EBO IS REALLY ILL. LET'S JUST PAY THE MONEY AND LEAVE.

OH, THIS ONE'S GOT ENOUGH MONEY TO BUY HIMSELF A PALACE.

THAT'S HIS MONEY, NOT YOURS. HIS BROTHER IS A GOOD SINGER AND HE EARNED IT.

LEAVE HIM ALONE.

CAN'T YOU SEE, HIS BROTHER'S ILL?

THANK YOU, THANK YOU.

WE'RE BUSINESSMEN, NOT CRIMINALS.

"WITHOUT MEDICINE, THAT KID WON'T LAST LONG."

I KNOW TRIPOLI.

YOU HAVE BEEN BEFORE?

I GOT THIS FAR ONCE BEFORE, BUT THEY CAUGHT ME AND TOOK ME BACK ACROSS THE DESERT TO TRY AGAIN.

"THERE ARE RULES FOR SURVIVAL IN TRIPOLI."

"STEER CLEAR OF THE STREET GANGS."

"HIDE YOUR MONEY SOMEWHERE SAFE."

"NEVER DRINK FROM STREET DRAINS."

"CAREFUL OF THE DOGS — SOME ARE RABID."

"WATCH OUT FOR THE ARMY."

"WATCH OUT FOR THE POLICE."

"WATCH OUT... FOR EVERYONE."

I KNOW SOMEWHERE WE CAN REST.

IT'S NOT A PROPER PLACE, BUT IT IS A FREE PLACE.

THIS IS A STORM DRAIN. IT FLOODS IF THERE'S A BIG RAIN, BUT THE REST OF THE YEAR YOU CAN SLEEP HERE.

HERE?

IT'S BETTER THAN GIVING MONEY FOR A ROOM TO SOMEONE YOU DON'T TRUST.

THERE'S NO ONE TO INFORM ON YOU.

WE CAN SAVE OUR MONEY FOR THE BOAT TO EUROPE.

THERE ARE MANY WAYS INSIDE. WE HAVE TO FIND ONE.

SOMEONE WAS THERE.

IT'S A GOOD PLACE. THERE MUST BE A WAY IN.

HERE ... LET'S GET HIM INSIDE.

HE NEEDS TO REST. BEING ON THE TRUCK DID NOT HELP HIM.

I hear voices. Kwame? Sisi?

DID WE GET TO EUROPE? IS SISI HERE?

I'm so cold.

YES, LITTLE BROTHER, SHE IS HERE. WE ALL MADE IT. NOW REST.

I HAVE TO GO AND FIND A FRIEND OF MINE. SEE IF HE'S STILL IN THE CITY.

HE MIGHT HAVE MADE EUROPE BY NOW.

I WILL TRY TO HELP.

STAY HERE. STAY HIDDEN.

DO NOT DIE, EBO. YOU ARE ALL I HAVE.

97

KWAME?

THERE WERE RATS ALL OVER HIM. HE'S GETTING WORSE.

I HAVE TO GET EBO TO A HOSPITAL.

KWAME, IF YOU GO INTO A HOSPITAL YOU CAN GET CAUGHT WITHOUT PAPERS AND ARRESTED.

I FOUND MY FRIEND. THIS IS NURU.

HE HAS A FRIEND WHO HAS A FRIEND THAT GOT HIM MEDICINE.

STOLEN MEDICINE?

IT MIGHT CURE HIS FEVER.

TAKING STOLEN MEDICINE IS NOT GOOD.

THE WRONG PILLS CAN KILL.

"HE'S YOUR BROTHER. IT'S YOUR CHOICE, KWAME. IT'S UP TO YOU."

NOW

CHAPTER 15

Everything is noise and chaos and water.

People scream.

Hardly anyone can swim.

I look for Kwame.

EBO!

My hand finds some floating wood from the ship and I hold on.

The woman pushes her baby at me.

What can I do?

Kwame!
What must
I do?

The helicopter.
The Europeans
will help.

They throw down orange bubble jackets.

EBO!

There are still people on the ship.

Trying to stay out of the water.

There's screaming from inside the ship.

People calling for help and then I realise...

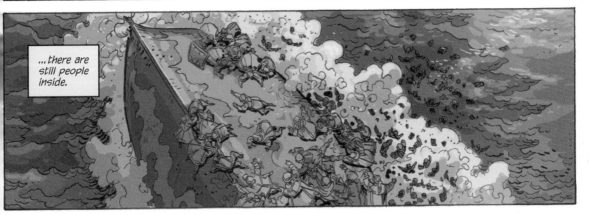

...there are still people inside.

And there's no way out.

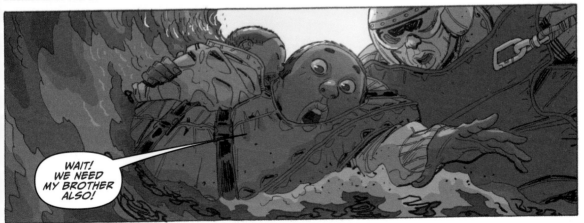

KWAME!

It will be Kwame's turn next.

He must be next.

KWAME!

Kwame!

I see Kwame go under.

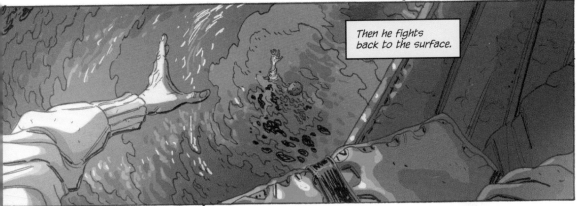

Then he fights back to the surface.

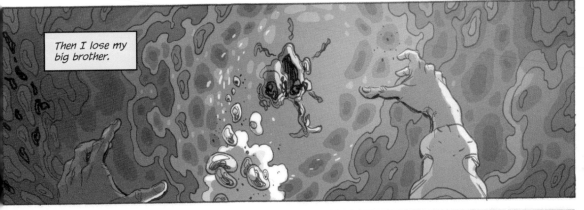

Then I lose my big brother.

I never see him again.

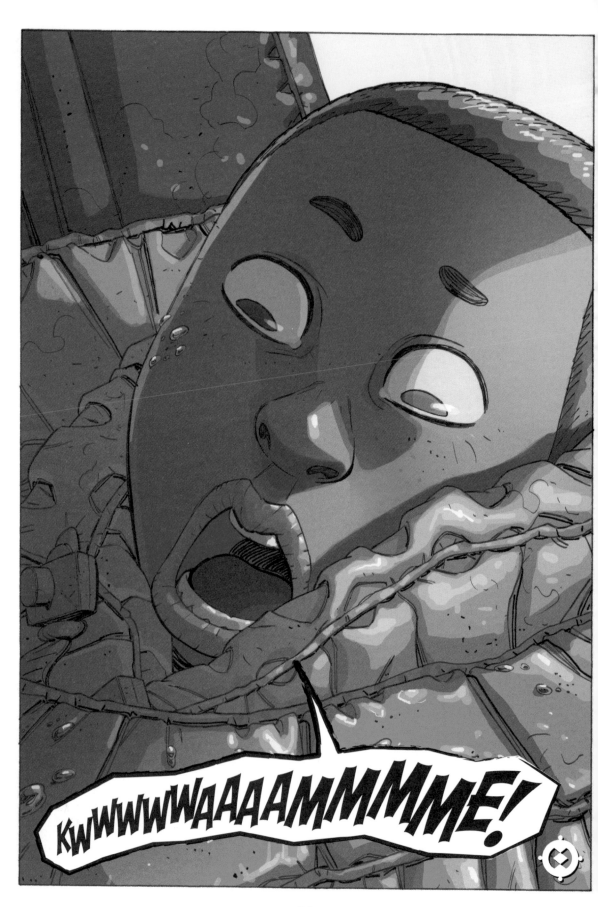

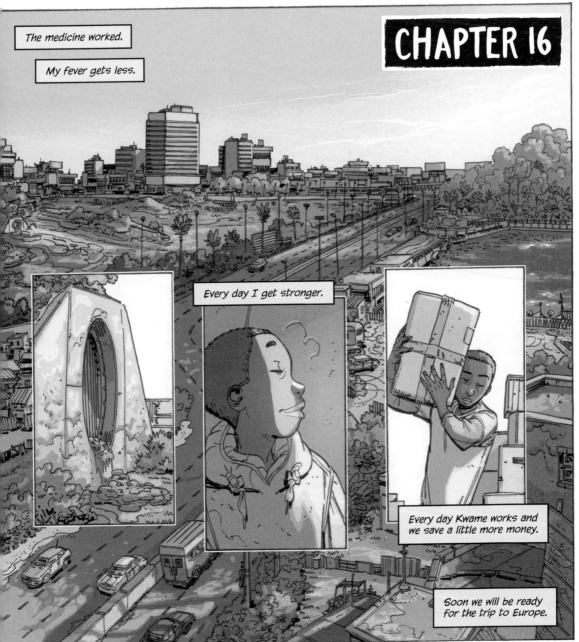

Razak and Nuru visit every evening.

EBO, HOW ARE YOU TODAY?

EVERY DAY I'M STRONGER, RAZAK.

They bring news of when boats are sailing.

When the men that run them are ready to move.

Every evening the talk goes round and round in circles.

LAST WEEK ALL THREE OF THE SHIPS OF THE SPANISH MEN MADE IT TO EUROPE. WE COULD MAKE A PASSAGE WITH THEM.

THEY MADE IT BECAUSE IT WAS PERFECT WEATHER. NO WIND AND NO CLOUD.

IF WE MAKE OUR PASSAGE WITH THEM WE MIGHT NOT BE SO LUCKY.

AND ANYWAY, WE DO NOT HAVE ENOUGH MONEY. IT'S TOO MUCH.

WE'RE SAVING EVERY DAY. WORKING, SINGING. WE CAN SAVE MORE AND THEN SAIL SAFELY.

IT'S ONLY SAFE IF THE WEATHER IS GOOD.

WE MUST RELY ON LUCK AND MANY PRAYERS.

THE LONGER WE HAVE TO STAY TO SAVE MONEY THEN THE MORE CHANCE ONE OF US IS CAUGHT WITHOUT PAPERS.

RAZAK, YOU HAVE ALREADY BEEN CAUGHT AND SENT BACK ACROSS THE DESERT.

YES, I HAVE BEATEN THE DESERT TWICE. I DO NOT THINK IT WILL LET ME WIN A THIRD TIME.

EVERY DAY WE STAY HERE IS A RISK. WE SHOULD GO TO EUROPE SOON.

THE TALL MAN'S PEOPLE SAY THEY HAVE A BOAT SAILING NEXT WEEK.

THEY'RE NO GOOD. THEY PROMISE PEOPLE A BIG SHIP AND THEN DELIVER A SMALL BALLOON BOAT.

THEY ARE NOT TO BE TRUSTED, I'VE HEARD IT TOO. LAST MONTH THEY LOST ALL THEIR BOATS.

YOU DON'T KNOW THAT FOR SURE.

I HEARD THAT NO ONE GOT A PHONE CALL. NOT ONE FAMILY!

WE NEED A PASSAGE THAT WE CAN AFFORD *AND* THAT IS SAFE.

LAST WEEK ALL THREE OF THE SHIPS OF THE SPANISH MEN MADE IT TO EUROPE.

WE COULD MAKE PASSAGE WITH THEM.

Every evening the talk goes round and round in circles.

We work.

We hide.

We sleep.

Something wakes us.

DID YOU JUST —

Soldiers.

We don't make a sound.

Until they go.

Before work, we go and find Razak.

THOSE SOLDIERS DIDN'T FIND THE WAY IN, BUT WE CAN'T STAY THERE MUCH LONGER.

THEY WILL BE BACK, I'M SURE.

DO TODAY'S WORK. GET YOUR MONEY READY.

I'LL FIND US THE NEXT BOAT.

SEE YOU TONIGHT.

BE VERY CAREFUL.

EBO, DID YOU HEAR THAT?

SOON...

I'M SCARED OF GOING. BUT I'M SCARED OF STAYING TOO.

ME TOO, LITTLE BROTHER.

We carry meat.

All day.

On the walk home, Kwame steps in a deep puddle and I remember...

RAIN!

REMEMBER WHAT RAZAK SAID HAPPENS WHEN IT RAINS?

THE DRAIN FLOODS. SO?

"OUR MONEY IS HIDDEN THERE..."

EBO! DON'T GO IN!

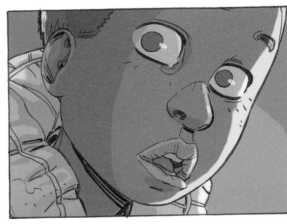

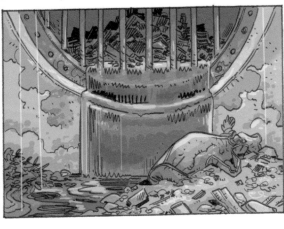

WE HAVE THE MONEY.

Razak makes a deal for us.

There's space on a boat leaving that night.

We are nervous but happy.

Europe is close.

They say a tiny balloon boat will take us to a bigger proper ship.

Kwame is worried, but Razak says we can trust them.

They do many crossings.

THANK YOU.

FOR WHAT?

IN JUST A FEW HOURS, WE WILL BE IN EUROPE. THAT WILL BE THANKS ENOUGH.

IN THE DRAIN. YOU SAVED ME AGAIN, BIG BROTHER.

NOW

REFUGEE CENTRE, ITALY

CHAPTER 17

I never see him again.

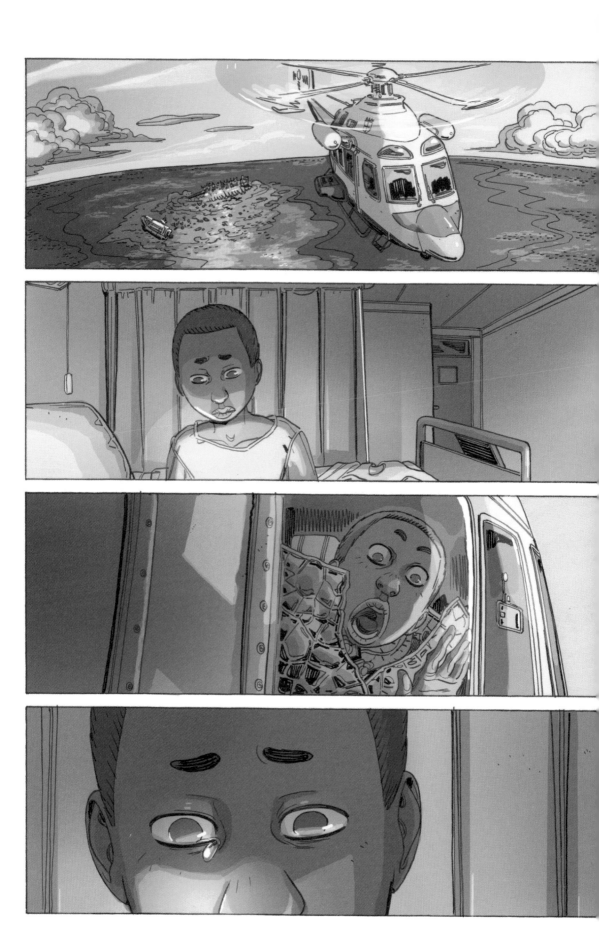

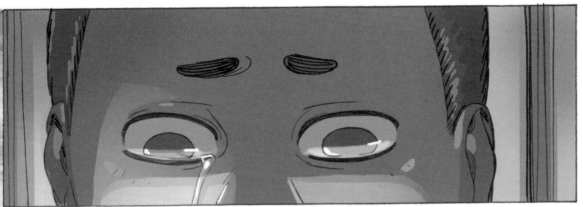

LONDON

In other news, hundreds more migrants have been rescued after their boat capsized in the Mediterranean Sea.

The ship, an unsafe fishing vessel, was reported as carrying over two hundred and fifty passengers when it capsized around twenty miles from the Italian coast.

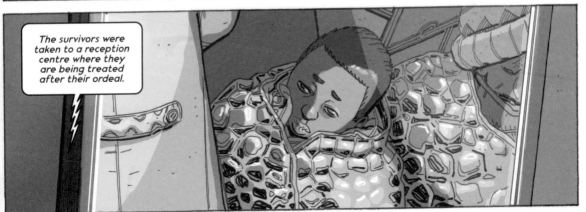

The survivors were taken to a reception centre where they are being treated after their ordeal.

EBO'S JOURNEY

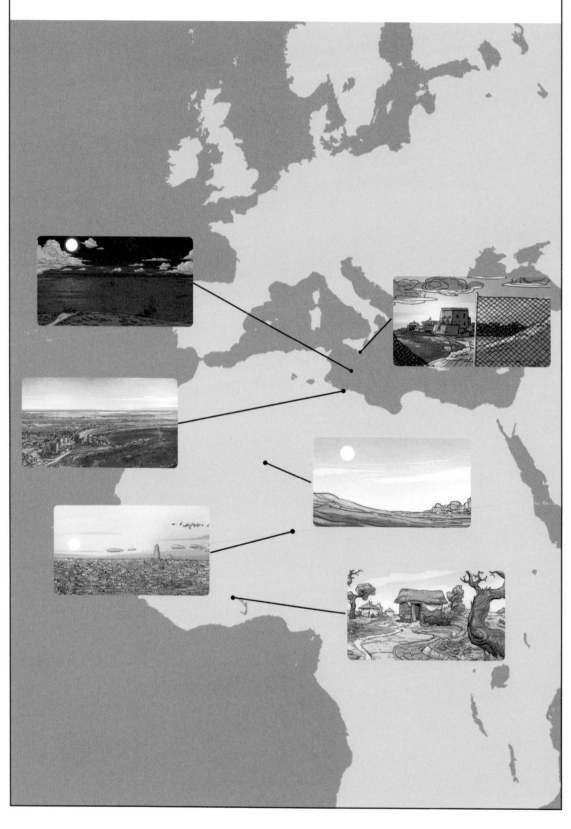

ILLEGAL

The story you've just read about Ebo's journey is a work of fiction, but every separate element of it is true.

Every year, many thousands of men, women, and children risk their lives by trying to make the dangerous 300-mile sea crossing between Northern Africa and Italy. They pay large sums of money to smugglers who in return provide poorly prepared unseaworthy boats. The distances involved are formidable and the sea currents are unpredictable. The smuggling networks that run these operations make fortunes with no regard for human life. They send their victims out to sea in death traps.

Many innocents die as a result, their loss of life often unknown and unrecorded. In 2015, more than a million migrants crossed the Mediterranean Sea to enter Europe. The United Nations has described the situation as a "colossal humanitarian catastrophe" and it is still going on.

The migrants come from different countries and travel for different reasons. Some are refugees fleeing war-torn countries like Syria. Others, like Ebo, are following family members in seeking a new life with better opportunities in Europe.

Most of the people trying to cross the Mediterranean Sea have already endured a long and dangerous journey. Crossing the Sahara Desert is just as dangerous as crossing the Mediterranean Sea. Broken trucks and broken promises mean many migrants lose their lives in the desert sands.

Many more migrants would perish in the Mediterranean without the daily search-and-rescue operations run by humanitarian organizations.

It's not a journey to be undertaken lightly. Every person making the choice to embark on that journey has their own reasons for doing so. And every person is a human being.

Eoin Colfer
Andrew Donkin
Giovanni Rigano

JOURNEY: HELEN'S STORY

Words by Helen as told
to Women for Refugee Women

Adapted for comics by
Colfer/Donkin/Rigano

I AM HELEN.

I WAS BORN IN ERITREA. MY MOTHER DIED WHEN I WAS YOUNG. MY FAMILY WERE SPLIT AND MY FATHER HAD TO FLEE. AT THE AGE OF 13, I WENT TO SUDAN TO LOOK FOR HIM AND ENDED UP STAYING THERE MANY YEARS.

I...

I LIVED IN HIDING, BECAUSE I DIDN'T HAVE ANY PAPERS. AN ELDERLY ETHIOPIAN WOMAN TOOK ME IN. I WORKED FOR HER MANY YEARS WITHOUT PAY BUT LAST YEAR SHE TOLD ME I HAD TO LEAVE.

"SHE KNEW SOME TRAFFICKERS WHO SAID THEY WOULD TAKE ME THROUGH THE DESERT, THROUGH LIBYA, AND ACROSS THE SEA TO ITALY, AND SHE MADE THE FIRST PAYMENT FOR ME."

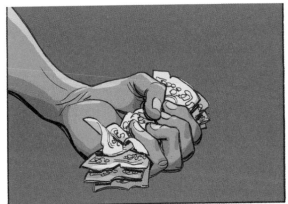

"WE CROSSED THE SAHARA DESERT IN A LORRY, TRAVELLING DAY AND NIGHT FOR 15 DAYS. IT WAS SO SANDY AND HOT."

"WE HAD BROUGHT FOOD AND WATER AND WE THOUGHT WE HAD WHAT WE NEEDED. THEN THE LORRY BROKE DOWN. THERE WAS NO SHADE — WE WERE BURNT BY THE SUN, AND THE CONSTANT HEAT MADE US MORE AND MORE THIRSTY."

ONE MAN LOST HIS BROTHER, AND A WOMAN I HAD KNOWN IN SUDAN ALSO DIED.

"WE TRIED TO BURY OUR FRIENDS. THE MEN DUG AND WE WOMEN WEPT. THOSE FRIENDS OF OURS WERE BURIED IN A SHALLOW GRAVE — IT WASN'T REALLY A BURIAL. THE SAND WILL NOT COVER THEM LONG."

"WHEN ANOTHER LORRY CAME FOR US IN THE DESERT, WE THOUGHT WE WERE BEING SAVED, BUT THESE MEN WERE TRAFFICKERS TOO."

THEY TOOK US TO LIBYA, WHICH WAS GOOD, BUT THEN THEY LOCKED US UP AND DEMANDED MONEY OR WE WOULD DIE.

"THEY GAVE ENOUGH FOOD SO WE WOULDN'T DIE, BUT NOT MUCH — WE WERE ALWAYS IN THE BALANCE BETWEEN LIFE AND DEATH."

I THOUGHT I WOULD NEVER MAKE IT OUT OF THAT PRISON, BECAUSE I HAD NO FAMILY I COULD CALL ON TO SEND MONEY FOR ME TO BE RELEASED.

"BUT MY FELLOW PRISONERS SAVED ME. WHEN THEY WERE ASKING THEIR FAMILIES TO SAVE THEM FROM THE PRISON, THEY ALSO ASKED FOR EXTRA MONEY TO GET ME OUT OF THERE."

WHEN WE SAILED, WE WERE LUCKY.

"THE BOAT BEHIND US, WHICH HAD OVER 400 PEOPLE IN, SANK. I KNEW SOME OF THE PEOPLE ON THERE."

"BUT THE ITALIAN SEA GUARDS MET OUR BOAT AND TOOK US TO ITALY. A COUPLE OF THE PEOPLE I WAS WITH SAID THAT THEY WERE TRAVELLING ON TO FRANCE TO TRY TO GET TO THE UK, AND ASKED ME IF I WANTED TO JOIN THEM."

"I WENT TO ISBERGUES, A CAMP NEAR TO CALAIS, AND LIVED THERE FOR TWO MONTHS. I WAS DESPERATE TO REACH A SAFE PLACE FOR ME. LIFE WAS HARD. BY NOW, I KNEW I WAS PREGNANT."

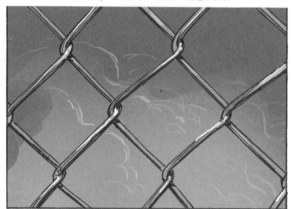

THERE WERE NO TOILETS, NO SHOWERS. FIVE OF US ON ONE MATTRESS. THERE WAS NO SLEEP BECAUSE DURING THE DAY PEOPLE WOULD COME AND GO, AND AT NIGHT I WOULD ALWAYS BE OUT TRYING TO GET ON THE LORRIES.

"BUT THERE WAS ONLY ONE THING ON MY MIND — THAT IF I GOT TO THE UK I WOULD REACH A SAFE PLACE WHERE I AND MY BABY COULD HAVE A GOOD CHANCE AT LIFE. I WAS DETERMINED TO GET HERE. I TRIED EVERY NIGHT WITHOUT FAIL."

"SO I CAME TO THIS COUNTRY HIDING IN A LORRY. 30 PEOPLE BROKE INTO THE SAME ONE AND HID. AT THE BORDER, THE LORRY WAS SEARCHED AND THE OTHER 29 PEOPLE WERE FOUND AND HAD TO GET OFF."

"I WAS UNDER THE FLOORING SO THEY COULDN'T FIND ME. UNKNOWINGLY, THE POLICE WERE WALKING ON TOP OF ME."

WHEN THE LORRY STOPPED I GOT UP AND KNEW THERE WAS SOMETHING WRONG.

"I WAS IN PAIN."

"THE LORRY DRIVER SHOUTED AT ME WHEN HE SAW ME, AND SAID HE COULDN'T DO ANYTHING TO HELP."

"THE POLICE TOOK ME TO THE HOSPITAL, BUT I HAD LOST MY BABY."

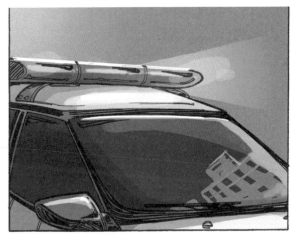

"NOW, I LIVE IN A HOSTEL IN LEEDS. I AM GIVEN MEALS BUT I DO NOT GET ANY MONEY AND I AM NOT ALLOWED TO WORK. I AM NOT COMPLAINING BECAUSE I HAVE BEEN IN SITUATIONS THAT WERE MUCH WORSE."

EVEN THOUGH I PASSED THROUGH ALL THAT SUFFERING, I AM HERE NOW, AND I AM THANKFUL FOR THAT.

I WANT TO BE EDUCATED. I DIDN'T HAVE MUCH OPPORTUNITY FOR LEARNING IN MY COUNTRY. I STOPPED GOING TO SCHOOL WHEN I WAS 12. I HOPE I CAN STUDY, BUT NOW I HAVE BECOME FORGETFUL. I DON'T REMEMBER THINGS. HOPEFULLY MY HEAD WILL START WORKING BETTER.

I WOULD LIKE TO BECOME A NURSE.

END

ACKNOWLEDGEMENTS

Research consultant: Vivien Francis

Grateful thanks to all the people who have given their time and energy and knowledge to help with this book especially:

Jo Adkins
Roberto Barrera
Sheila Brand
Jax Burgoyne
Paul Chapman
Miles Dennison
Mike Fillis
Jamie Finch
Ron Fogelman
Dr Thomas Giddens
Sophie Hicks
Matthew Pennycook MP
Moe Redish
Antonio Scricco
Will Vunderink
Sarah Williams

The Estate of Elie Wiesel

Our lovely team at Hodder:
Anne McNeil
Alison Padley
Rachel Wade

The staff at the Cairo Library & Archive at the National Maritime Museum, Greenwich.

SPECIAL THANKS TO ALL THE PEOPLE WHO
TALKED TO US ABOUT THEIR EXPERIENCES BUT
WHO WISHED TO REMAIN ANONYMOUS.

AND A HUGE THANK YOU TO THE FOLLOWING
INDIVIDUALS AND THEIR CHARITIES:

ANNE STOLTENBERG AND NAZEK RAMADAN AT
MIGRANT VOICE
WWW.MIGRANTVOICE.ORG

NATASHA WALTER AND MARCHU GIRMA AT
WOMEN FOR REFUGEE WOMEN
WWW.REFUGEEWOMEN.CO.UK

HELEN MEAD AT GREENWICH MIGRANT HUB
WWW.GREENWICHMIGRANTHUB.COM

EBO

KWAME

SISI

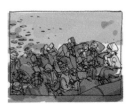

EOIN COLFER (PRONOUNCED OWEN) WAS BORN IN WEXFORD ON THE SOUTH-EAST COAST OF IRELAND IN 1965. HE FIRST DEVELOPED AN INTEREST IN WRITING WHEN HE WAS GRIPPED BY THE VIKING STORIES HE LEARNED ABOUT AT SCHOOL. AFTER HIS MARRIAGE, HE AND HIS WIFE SPENT ABOUT FOUR YEARS WORKING IN SAUDI ARABIA, TUNISIA AND ITALY. HIS FIRST BOOK, **BENNY AND OMAR**, WAS BASED ON HIS EXPERIENCES IN TUNISIA; IT HAS SINCE BEEN TRANSLATED INTO MANY LANGUAGES. IN 2001 THE FIRST **ARTEMIS FOWL** BOOK WAS PUBLISHED AND EOIN GAVE UP TEACHING TO CONCENTRATE FULLY ON WRITING. EOIN, WHO LIVES IN IRELAND WITH HIS WIFE AND TWO CHILDREN, SAYS, 'I WILL KEEP WRITING UNTIL PEOPLE STOP READING OR I RUN OUT OF IDEAS. HOPEFULLY NEITHER OF THESE WILL HAPPEN ANYTIME SOON.'

ANDREW DONKIN HAS SOLD OVER EIGHT MILLION CHILDREN'S BOOKS, GRAPHIC NOVELS, AND ADULT BOOKS. HIS WORK IN COMICS INCLUDES BATMAN: **LEGENDS OF THE DARK KNIGHT** FOR DC COMICS, AND **DOCTOR WHO**. WITH EOIN COLFER, HE HAS CO-WRITTEN FIVE BESTSELLING GRAPHIC NOVEL ADAPTATIONS OF EOIN'S BOOKS. ANDREW BECAME INTERESTED IN THE ISSUE OF MIGRANTS AND ASYLUM WHILE WRITING THE BIOGRAPHY OF SIR ALFRED MEHRAN, A STATELESS MAN WHO LIVED ON A BENCH IN PARIS AIRPORT FOR 18 YEARS. THE RESULTING BOOK, **THE**

TERMINAL MAN, WAS DESCRIBED BY THE SUNDAY TIMES AS 'A BRILLIANT AND PROFOUNDLY DISTURBING BOOK.' ANDREW LIVES NEAR THE RIVER THAMES IN LONDON WITH HIS FAMILY.

GIOVANNI RIGANO IS AN ITALIAN COMICS ARTIST AND CREATOR OF MANY GRAPHIC NOVELS. HE HAS ADAPTED FIVE OF EOIN COLFER'S NOVELS INTO GRAPHIC NOVELS AS WELL AS DISNEY-PIXAR'S **THE INCREDIBLES**, THREE **PIRATES OF THE CARIBBEAN** NOVELS, AND HIS OWN SERIES **DAFFODIL**. HE LIVES IN COMO, ITALY.